I Like It.

Written by Richard Daraja

Illustrated by
Deborah Melmon

Scott Foresman

My pet is a bird.

The bird can sing.

The bird can fly!

My pet is a dog.

The dog can kiss me.

The dog can run!

 My pet is a fish.

The fish is in a bowl.

The fish can swim!

Pets can do a lot.

I like pets.